TIGERS, TOO
SUPPLEMENT

CHECKLISTS FOR CLASSROOM OBJECTIVES AND INTERVENTIONS

TIGERS, TOO
SUPPLEMENT

CHECKLISTS FOR CLASSROOM OBJECTIVES AND INTERVENTIONS

OBJECTIVES AND INTERVENTIONS APPROPRIATE FOR CHALLENGES
MANY STUDENTS EXPERIENCE AS THE CONSEQUENCE OF IMPAIRED
EXECUTIVE FUNCTIONS, PROCESSING SPEED, AND MEMORY.

MARILYN P. DORNBUSH, PH.D.

SHERYL K. PRUITT, M.ED., ET/P

Parkaire Press
Atlanta

Parkaire Press, Inc.
4939 Lower Roswell Road, Building C
Marietta, Georgia 30068-4328
www.parkairepress.com

Publisher's Cataloging-in-Publication
(Provided by Quality Books, Inc.)

Dornbush, Marilyn Pierce, 1933-
    Tigers, too. Supplement: checklists for classroom
objectives and interventions / Marilyn P. Dornbush,
Sheryl K. Pruitt.
        p. cm.
    "Executive functions/speed of processing/memory.
Impact on academic, behavioral, and social functioning
of students with ADHD, Tourette syndrome, and OCD."
    LCCN 2010912638
    ISBN-13: 978-0-9818643-4-1
    ISBN-10: 0-9818643-4-1

    1. Attention-deficit-disordered children--Education--
United States--Handbooks, manuals, etc.
2. Attention-deficit hyperactivity disorder--United States
--Handbooks, manuals, etc. 3. Tourette syndrome in
children--United States--Handbooks, manuals, etc.
4. Obsessive-compulsive disorder in children--United States
--Handbooks, manuals, etc. I. Pruitt, Sheryl K.,
1944- II. Title.

    LC4713.4.D675 2010   371.94
              QBI10-600169

Cover designed by Mayapriya Long, Bookwright Press, Inc.

Photograph of Julianna by Shari Zellers Photography, Atlanta. Other photos by Istockphoto.com. All of the children on the cover are models. Use of their photos is not intended to suggest that they have any of the disorders discussed in this guide.

10 9 8 7 6 5 4 3 2 1

Printed in the United States of America

TABLE OF CONTENTS

PREFACE

This book is a supplement to *Tigers, Too*, which offers comprehensive recommendations for addressing deficits associated with executive dysfunction, slow processing speed, and memory problems; impairments which often interfere with a student's academic, behavioral, and social functioning. When planning workable solutions to handle these difficulties, individuals involved in the education of the student can readily answer the "who," "what," "when," and "where" of the problem. An in depth assessment identifies "why." Answering the question of "how" is more problematic. *Tigers, Too* provides numerous intervention strategies; however, the suggestions are not appropriate for all students. It is the responsibility of teachers, parents, and other professionals working with each individual student to set specific goals, to consider solutions to the student's problems, to analyze the positive and negative consequences of each idea, and to determine strategies which can be carried out efficiently and successfully.

Checklists of Objectives and Interventions was designed as an aide for identifying, organizing, and developing an effective educational program for the individual student. The outline of the book is based on the one established in *Tigers, Too* (arousal and speed of processing; attention, inhibition, and activity level; executive function; memory; the seven areas of academic proficiency; study skills; testing; and social competence). The checklist includes interventions that personnel who are involved in the process of trying to meet the needs of the student might consider and implement.

- 🐾 *Teachers and parents must also share their own ideas and suggestions for decreasing the impact of these disorders on the student's academic, behavioral, and social functioning.*

- 🐾 *Page numbers refer the reader to the appropriate section(s) in **Tigers, Too**.*

These pages may be reprinted for personal use.

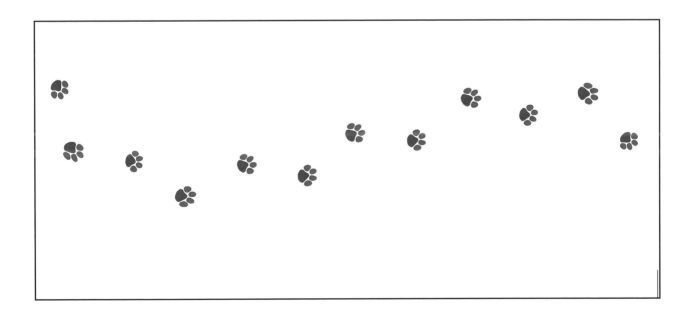

SECTION I

UNDERAROUSAL

SLOW COGNITIVE PROCESSING SPEED

UNDERAROUSAL/SLOW COGNITIVE PROCESSING SPEED

Tigers, Too (pp. 27-28, 71-78)

Objective

To increase the student's level of arousal and speed of processing

Interventions

_____ With teacher instruction and cueing, the student will learn strategies for recognizing and modifying arousal levels.

      _____ take mobility breaks between tasks

      _____ exercise muscles and joints (e.g., press hands together, do chair push ups, push against the wall, carry reasonably heavy box to office)

      _____ use the computer to increase interest and alertness

      _____ have a protein snack

      _____ chew gum

      _____ other _____

_____ With teacher providing cognitive cues and practice, the student will master academic skills: (_____ basic reading skills, _____ reading comprehension, _____ spelling and writing skills, _____ math computation, _____ math reasoning skills) at an automatic level (90% over an extended period of time).

_____ With teacher assistance, the student will:

      _____ complete untimed assignments.

      _____ answer a reduced number of questions.

      _____ participate in cooperative learning activities.

      _____ alternate between seatwork and classroom learning centers.

      _____ use games and hands-on projects.

      _____ use a word processor, _____ calculator, and/or _____ tape recorder.

_____ With teacher accommodations, the student will take tests:

      _____ in segments and administered at different times.

      _____ in _____ multiple-choice, _____ matching, and/or _____ true-false formats rather than fill-in-the-blank, short answer, or essay formats.

      _____ using a word bank.

      _____ answering open-book or take-home test questions.

      _____ creating an outline to answer essay questions.

      _____ using graphic organizers to answer essay questions.

      _____ orally.

SECTION II

ANXIETY

"STORMS"/OVERAROUSAL

ANXIETY/"STORMS"/OVERAROUSAL

Tigers, Too (pp. 79-95)

ANXIETY

Objective

To reduce the student's anxiety level

Interventions

_____ With teacher scheduling, the student will follow a structured classroom routine.

_____ With teacher assistance, the student will:
_____ participate in cooperative rather than competitive activities.
_____ work in small groups.
_____ pair with a classmate when _____ completing assignments, _____ taking tests, _____ doing homework.

_____ With teacher assistance and cueing, the student will:
_____ take a movement break.
_____ change activities.
_____ move to a less stressful work area.
_____ select and use a relaxation technique.
_____ breathing exercises or relaxation techniques
_____ counting to 10
_____ progressively relaxing
_____ visualizing
_____ listening to calming music
_____ go to a prearranged safe place when feeling overwhelmed and anxious.

_____ With teacher assistance, the student will:
_____ determine events that lead to an anxiety reaction.
_____ identify and reframe negative cognitions.
_____ learn a script or strategy to use when anxiety becomes overwhelming.
_____ select a strategy for handling situations that precipitate anxiety.
_____ make positive rather than negative self-statements.
_____ reward self for efforts to control anxiety.

Section II

"STORMS"/OVERAROUSAL

Objective

To improve the student's ability to manage overarousal and prevent "storms"

Interventions

_____ With teacher assistance, the student will when overstimulated by the classroom arrangement:
- _____ sit at a desk near the teacher and where most teaching occurs.
- _____ move to a pre-assigned desk at the rear of the room.
- _____ change to a different but designated work space.
- _____ complete assignments in a study area separated from the rest of the class (e.g., carrel).
- _____ follow the rules for moving between work sites.

_____ With teacher assistance, the student will select a "buddy" to help alleviate some of the stress associated with the disorder(s). The student will choose a:
- _____ work-completion "buddy."
- _____ note taking "buddy."
- _____ homework "buddy."
- _____ cafeteria "buddy."
- _____ playground "buddy."
- _____ bus "buddy."

_____ With teacher assistance and cueing, the student will appropriately use mobility options.
- _____ change work sites
- _____ stand up and stretch
- _____ perform a resistive physical activity (e.g., press hands together, do chair pushups, push against the wall, carry reasonably heavy box to office)
- _____ go on an errand for the teacher

_____ The student will complete seatwork at the student's <u>independent</u> level (_____ grade level).

_____ With teacher assistance and practice, the student will learn and use a cognitive self-talk problem-solving technique.
- _____ recognize problem situations
- _____ identify factors that caused the problems
- _____ discuss consequences of previous behaviors (positive and negative) in similar situations
- _____ use the who, what, when, where, how, and why questions to understand the nature of the problems
- _____ set short-term and long-term goals that address problems.
- _____ generate (brainstorm) solutions to problems
- _____ correctly prioritize problems to be addressed
- _____ analyze the consequences of each proposed idea
- _____ decide on and use the best strategy

_____ self-monitor the implementation of the strategy and self-correct as needed

_____ evaluate the results of the changes in behavior

_____ accept, make, and internalize positive statements about the results of changes in behavior

_____ With teacher assistance, the student will learn and successfully use a strategy for identifying and responding to unintentional physical contact.

_____ With teacher assistance, the student when hypersensitive to touch will participate in an alternate activity that does not require physical contact.

_____ With teacher instruction and assistance, the student will learn how to appropriately touch another peer.

_____ With teacher instruction and assistance, the student will learn and use a strategy for responding appropriately to provocation.

_____ With teacher assistance and cueing, the student will use a known strategy to avoid escalating negative situations.

_____ With teacher assistance and cueing, the student will identify signs of impending loss of control (e.g., feeling anxious, tightening of stomach, flushing of face).

_____ With teacher assistance and cueing, the student will verbalize feelings rather than engage in angry, aggressive behaviors.

_____ With teacher assistance and practice, the student will use strategies to release feelings of frustration and anger before losing control.

_____ use self-talk

_____ write about or draw angry feelings

_____ hit an "angry pillow" in a designated safe place

_____ utilize a calming technique:

_____ deep breathing

_____ progressively relaxing

_____ visualizing

_____ listening to calming music

_____ drawing/writing thoughts and feelings

_____ talking with trusted friend or adult

_____ When confronted with an emotionally charged academic situation, the student will leave the setting in a previously agreed-upon manner and go to a prearranged safe place to release frustration and anger.

     _____ resource room

     _____ school psychologist's office

     _____ nurse's office

     _____ principal's office

     _____ other _____

_____ With teacher assistance and cueing, the student will use a previously agreed-upon strategy for responding to correction and failure.

_____ With teacher assistance and cueing, the student will use a previously agreed-upon strategy for accepting adult intervention in emotionally charged situations.

_____ With teacher assistance and cueing and after calm has been restored, the student will:

     _____ identify the effect of inappropriate behavior on others.

     _____ clean up any damage and/or correct any problems that may have resulted from loss of control.

     _____ initiate an apology for inappropriate behavior.

     _____ verbalize solutions to mend a damaged:

          _____ peer relationship.

          _____ teacher relationship.

          _____ adult relationship.

_____ With teacher assistance, cueing, and practice, the student will use alternatives to resolve conflicts (e.g., negotiation).

SECTION III

INATTENTION

IMPULSIVITY

HYPERACTIVITY

INATTENTION/IMPULSIVITY/HYPERACTIVITY

Tigers, Too (pp. 28, 97-105)

INATTENTION

Objective

To minimize the student's difficulty focusing and sustaining attention and resisting distractions

Interventions

_____ With teacher assistance and to minimize distractions, the student will:

    _____ sit away from noisy, busy areas.

    _____ work in small group settings.

    _____ work with a "buddy."

    _____ use a headset with _____ white noise or _____ music.

    _____ study in a carrel.

_____ With teacher cueing, the student will attend to instructions before beginning to work. The student will:

    _____ repeat and paraphrase directions.

    _____ demonstrate understanding of instructions.

    _____ highlight, _____ underline, and/or _____ circle cue words in written instructions.

_____ The student will complete class assignments and homework at the student's independent level (_____ grade level).

_____ With teacher assistance and practice, the student will use self-talk (subvocalization) to help maintain attention.

_____ With teacher instruction, practice, and cueing, the student will recognize a prearranged hand signal or gesture that serves as a reminder of on-task behavior.

_____ The student will independently verbalize and employ a previously learned strategy to return to task.

_____ When symptoms of the disorder(s) impact the ability to attend, the student will with teacher assistance:

    _____ complete short tasks that require accuracy and quality of response.

    _____ review previously learned skills.

    _____ use the computer to reinforce learning.

    _____ retreat to a prearranged safe place.

_____ When off-task behaviors interfere with the rest of the class, the student will respond to:

     _____ cueing as a signal to jump-start attention.

     _____ redirection by the teacher.

     _____ time-out _____ voluntarily or _____ when cued to regain control in a pre-arranged safe place.

IMPULSIVITY

Objective

To improve the student's ability to control impulsive responding

Interventions

_____ With teacher assistance, the student will complete short tasks with a criterion for accuracy.

_____ With teacher instruction and assistance, the student will use a strategy to self-monitor impulse control.

     _____ verbal cue

     _____ visual cue

     _____ cognitive cue

_____ With teacher instruction and cueing, the student will use self-talk (subvocalization) to reduce impulsivity.

_____ With teacher instruction and assistance, the student will learn turn-taking strategies by:

     _____ practicing turn-taking in teacher-directed lessons.

     _____ participating in small groups which provide frequent opportunities to interact.

     _____ observing the nonverbal cues indicating that classmates are annoyed with interruptions.

_____ When unable to inhibit behavior, the student will, after calm has been restored, repair any damage to:

     _____ relationships.

     _____ property.

HYPERACTIVITY

Objective

To improve the student's ability to maintain an appropriate activity level

Interventions

_____ With teacher assistance, the student will appropriately use mobility options throughout the day. The student will:

      _____ change work sites.

      _____ leave the classroom (e.g., carry a heavy box to a designated place, make a trip to the office, take a note to another teacher).

      _____ hand out materials, collect papers.

      _____ use a small squeeze toy that is silent and does not roll.

      _____ doodle.

      _____ stand up, stretch, twist, etc.

      _____ run around the track.

      _____ throw a ball.

      _____ sit on a therapy ball.

Tigers, Too: Checklists © 2010 by Marilyn P. Dornbush, Ph.D., and Sheryl K. Pruitt, M.Ed., ET/P

SECTION IV

EXECUTIVE DYSFUNCTION

EXECUTIVE DYSFUNCTION

Tigers, Too (pp. 29-33, 107-130)

IMPAIRED PROBLEM SOLVING

DIFFICULTY SETTING GOALS

Objective

To improve the student's ability to set realistic long-term and short-term goals

Interventions

_____ With teacher assistance and practice, the student will use a template of a strategy for setting goals.

_____ With teacher assistance and practice, the student will define a task, activity, or problem situation in concrete, concise terms.

_____ With teacher assistance and practice, the student will break a task, activity, or problem situation into its various parts and identify what needs to be accomplished.

_____ With teacher assistance and practice, the student will set long-term goals.

_____ With teacher assistance and practice, the student will set realistic, clear, and explicitly stated short-term goals.

_____ The student will repeatedly state and cue each step of goal setting.

_____ The student will check with an adult to determine whether the goals are realistic.

DIFFICULTY PLANNING

Objective

To improve the student's ability to plan a strategy for solving a task, activity, or problem situation

Intervention

_____ With teacher assistance and practice, the student will devise a plan for accomplishing the goal(s).

Tigers, Too: Checklists © 2010 by Marilyn P. Dornbush, Ph.D., and Sheryl K. Pruitt, M.Ed., ET/P

DIFFICULTY PROPOSING OR GENERATING IDEAS/STRATEGIES/SOLUTIONS

Objective

To improve the student's ability to generate practical and useful ideas, strategies, solutions to achieve the goal(s)

Interventions

_____ With teacher assistance and practice, the student will activate existing knowledge and personal experiences related to the academic task, activity, or problem situation.

_____ With teacher assistance and practice, the student will:

      _____ define an academic skill, task, or activity.

      _____ self-evaluate mastery of the academic skill.

      _____ identify prerequisites to the skill which have not been learned.

      _____ discuss what the skill is, <u>when</u>, <u>where</u>, and <u>how</u> it might be used, and <u>why</u> learning it is important.

_____ With teacher assistance and practice, the student will:

      _____ think about <u>who</u> and <u>what</u> were responsible for a problem situation.

      _____ determine <u>when</u> and <u>where</u> the problem happened.

      _____ discuss possible reasons <u>how</u> and <u>why</u> the problem occurred.

_____ With teacher assistance and practice, the student will generate ideas/solutions/strategies by:

      _____ using a mind mapping program.

      _____ tape recording.

      _____ drawing cartoons.

      _____ brainstorming with a classmate who excels in creating original ideas.

_____ With teacher assistance, the student will discuss and analyze both the positive and negative outcomes or consequences of each idea or solution.

_____ With teacher assistance and practice, the student will select the best idea, solution, or strategy.

DIFFICULTY PRIORITIZING

Objective

To improve the student's ability to prioritize tasks and activities

Interventions

_____ With teacher assistance, the student will prioritize _____ 2, _____ 3, _____ 4, _____ 5 tasks, choices, or options.

_____ With teacher assistance and cueing, the student will identify and state the importance and purpose of skills, strategies, or information.

_____ With teacher assistance, the student will learn and be able to respond to words or phrases that emphasize importance (e.g., "Listen carefully, ... " "It's important to know that . . . . " "In conclusion, ... ").

_____ With teacher assistance and cueing, the student will identify the most important information presented (e.g., answers to questions, main ideas, related facts).

_____ With teacher assistance and practice, the student will:
_____ repeat main ideas.
_____ rephrase key concepts.
_____ summarize essential ideas.

_____ With teacher assistance, cueing, and practice the student will listen for the who, what, when, where, how, and why of information.

_____ With teacher assistance, the student will use a lettered or numbered outline to list relevant concepts and facts.

_____ With teacher assistance, the student will use a lettered or numbered mind map or other graphic organizer to indicate main ideas and related details.

_____ With teacher assistance and practice, the student will prepare short "To Do Lists" to organize, prioritize, and consolidate all of the essential tasks that need to be carried out during the day, week, and month.

DIFFICULTY ORGANIZING

Objective

To improve the student's organizational skills

Interventions

_____ With teacher assistance, the student will use graphic organizers to visually structure and organize ideas and concepts. The student will use:
_____ who, what, when, where, how, and why outlines to represent problems, solutions used, and their outcomes.
_____ mind maps to depict main ideas, subtopics, details.
_____ timelines to describe a sequence of events, steps in a process, stages of something, or historical events/dates.
_____ Venn diagrams to express similarities and differences between ideas, people, places, events, or concepts.
_____ circles to show how sequences of related events occur repeatedly to produce results that are self-reinforcing.
_____ tables.
_____ bar graphs.
_____ pie graphs.

_____ flow charts.

_____ With teacher assistance, the student will maintain an organized notebook. The student will:

    _____ label subject dividers in order of student's schedule.

    _____ place a tabbed divider for each subject.

    _____ color code tabbed dividers and book covers with the same color.

    _____ put a photocopy of the teacher's notes following each class divider.

    _____ place paper for taking notes behind each divider.

    _____ date all notes and place them in chronological order.

    _____ insert at the end of each section a labeled, color-coordinated, manila folder with a pocket on each side and use one side for class handouts and the other for homework.

_____ With teacher assistance, the student will select or design an assignment book.

_____ With teacher assistance, the student will securely place the assignment book in the front of the notebook.

_____ With teacher assistance, the student will:

    _____ write all assignments in the assignment book.

    _____ get copies of assignments and put them in the notebook.

    _____ get copies of notes from a note taking "buddy."

    _____ tape record assignments.

    _____ receive assignments via email.

_____ With teacher cueing, the student will ask the teacher to review and sign the assignment book.

_____ With teacher assistance, the student will organize and keep track of assignments, materials, and belongings.

_____ With teacher assistance, the student will maintain a filing system to keep old tests, quizzes, and handouts for use when preparing for cumulative exams.

_____ With teacher assistance, all personal belongings will be labeled with the student's name.

_____ With teacher assistance and cueing, the student will organize materials at a designated time during the day.

_____ With teacher assistance and cueing, the student will follow a weekly routine for cleaning out and reorganizing notebooks, folders, desks, lockers, and other possessions.

_____ With teacher assistance and cueing, the student will organize materials needed for homework assignments.

_____ The student will use a locker that has _____ a lock with a key or _____ a combination lock that requires no reverse sequencing.

_____ The student will store books and materials in a designated area rather than in the locker.

_____ With the assistance of an aide, the student will go to the locker two to three minutes before the end of the day to avoid the confusion of a noisy, crowded hallway.

_____ With the assistance of the teacher or an aide, the student will check a list of needed homework materials that has been placed at eye level inside the locker.

_____ With the assistance of an aide or resource teacher, the student will ask for the school bag to be checked to ensure the necessary items are included.

_____ Given a class or homework assignment and _____ teacher prompts, the student will turn in class assignments and homework.

DIFFICULTY SEQUENCING

Objective

To improve the student's sequencing skills

Interventions

_____ With teacher cueing, the student will learn sequencing words (e.g., "before," "after," "first," "second," "next," "then," and "finally").

_____ With teacher assistance and practice, the student will relate personal stories using sequencing words.

_____ With teacher assistance, the student will practice sequencing and use cue words to indicate the steps by:
_____ planning and carrying out a multi-step task.
_____ playing classroom games.
_____ cutting up comic strips and arranging the sections in the correct order.
_____ playing computer games involving sequencing (e.g., doing construction projects, planning an adventure).

_____ With teacher assistance and practice, the student will follow a list or an outline of the steps required to complete an assignment, research paper, or long-term project.

_____ With teacher assistance and practice, the student will use cognitive sequencing cues for abstract academic sequences.

_____ With teacher cueing, the student will ask for help determining whether the correct sequence is being followed before completing classwork or homework.

_____ With teacher direction, the student will place sequencing strategies in the strategy ("trick") book.

DIFFICULTY MANAGING TIME

Objective

To improve the student's ability to organize and manage time

Interventions

_____ With teacher assistance and practice, the student will develop an awareness of the amount of time spent on daily activities.

_____ With teacher assistance and practice, the student will be able to write down the time needed to complete academic tasks and check the accuracy of the estimates when the tasks are finished.

_____ With teacher assistance and practice, the student will be able to monitor the passage of time while completing class assignments. The student will:

> _____ use a timer or stopwatch.

> _____ acknowledge the remaining time when reminded 15 minutes, 10 minutes, and 5 minutes prior to the end of an activity.

_____ With teacher assistance and practice, the student will analyze and discuss the appropriateness of the time spent.

_____ With teacher assistance, the student will use daily and weekly schedules/planners and monthly calendars.

_____ The student will _____ select or _____ design the daily and weekly schedules and monthly calendars.

_____ The student will use an electronic organizer:

> _____ a voice-activated model.

> _____ an organizer that provides external, time-based prompts (electronically activated screen, beeps, vibrations) to cue important activities.

> _____ a pocket-size electronic model that visually displays daily and weekly schedules and calendar on a screen.

_____ With teacher assistance and practice, the student will prepare short "To Do Lists." The student will transfer the "To Do Lists" to the daily and weekly schedules and monthly calendars. The student will:

> _____ prioritize, organize, and consolidate all of the essential tasks that need to be carried out during the day, week, and month.

> _____ balance social activities with academic responsibilities.

> _____ sequence activities in the order in which they occur throughout the day.

> _____ estimate and allocate the time it will take to complete the tasks and schedule accordingly.

> _____ schedule breaks between tasks.

_____ note due dates and steps for completing long-term assignments and for studying for tests.

_____ highlight steps for completing a book report in one color, test dates in another color, etc.

_____ follow the study schedule for completing reports, long-term projects, and tests.

_____ cross off tasks as they are completed.

_____ determine at frequently scheduled check points whether the timeline is being followed.

_____ With teacher assistance and cueing, the student will discuss the list as it is being prepared.

_____ With teacher assistance, the student will place the daily and weekly schedules and monthly calendars in the front of the student's notebook.

_____ With teacher cueing, the student will frequently consult the classroom daily and weekly schedules and monthly calendars that are posted at eye level in the front of the classroom.

_____ The student will consult with an academic assistant/tutor on a daily basis regarding schedules and time management.

DIFFICULTY BEING FLEXIBLE

Objective

To improve the student's ability to shift between ideas, emotions, tasks, activities, and situations

Interventions

_____ With teacher assistance, the student will, when possible, successfully transition between academic tasks and activities.

_____ With teacher cueing, the student will follow a structured classroom routine.

_____ With teacher assistance, cueing, and practice, the student will when perseverating on one thought or feeling (being "stuck"):

_____ identify and analyze the problem.

_____ discuss the situation that produced inflexibility.

_____ use a self-talk strategy to rephrase thinking.

_____ change the activity.

_____ take a movement break.

_____ use a breathing exercise or relaxation technique.

_____ move to a prearranged safe area if the emotion is overwhelming.

_____ With teacher assistance and cueing, the student will, if possible, use a previously learned strategy to shift when perseverating on just one thought or emotion.

_____ With teacher assistance, the student will preview plans for future activities and events (e.g., fire drills, assemblies, field trips, change of schools) and discuss expectations.

_____ With teacher assistance, the student will prearrange a strategy for avoiding trouble if a problem arises working with a substitute teacher. The student will go to a predetermined site of the student's choice.

     _____ resource room

     _____ nurse's office

     _____ counselor's office

     _____ school psychologist's office

     _____ principal's office

     _____ other _____

_____ The student will verbally acknowledge advance notices of impending transitions.

_____ With teacher assistance, the student will prepare for a change of schools.

     _____ master the use of daily, weekly, and monthly schedules

     _____ learn organizational strategies that promote independent functioning

     _____ practice changing classes

     _____ role play situations that might occur at the new school

     _____ visit the new school

     _____ accompany a student at the school for one day

     _____ obtain information about the school from its website

DIFFICULTY INITIATING/EXECUTING TASKS

Objective

To improve the student's ability to initiate and complete tasks

Interventions

_____ When given an assignment at the independent level (_____ grade level) and a _____ verbal, _____ visual, or _____ cognitive cue, the student will initiate work on assignments.

_____ When given directions or an assignment which the student does not understand, the student will initiate asking for help.

_____ With teacher assistance, the student will complete assignments.

_____ The student will ask the teacher to review the assignment and to list remaining items that need to be finished.

_____ The student will check off items as they are completed.

_____ The student will consult with an adult to determine whether a report or project is complete before turning it in to the teacher.

_____ After an absence, the student will ask the teacher to devise a plan for completing the missed work.

_____ The student will follow the teacher-initiated schedule for completing the assignments.

DIFFICULTY SELF-MONITORING/USING FEEDBACK/SELF-CORRECTING

Objective

To improve the student's ability to self-monitor, use feedback, and self-correct

Interventions

_____ With teacher assistance, the student will discuss, identify, and become aware of personal strengths and challenges that interfere with academic performance. The student will:

_____ predict performance prior to initiating tasks.

_____ grade assignments and explain how the grades were derived.

_____ record the number of correct answers and compare the results over time.

_____ praise or reward self if the predictions were accurate.

_____ With teacher assistance and practice, the student will use self-questioning to monitor:

_____ academic performance.

_____ behavioral control.

_____ social interactions.

_____ With teacher assistance, the student will generate a checklist of questions to serve as a visual guide when self-monitoring.

_____ Following prompt, specific, and corrective feedback, the student will make corrections and persist until an assignment is corrected.

_____ With teacher assistance, the student will use correction strategies.

_____ editing strips

_____ spelling lists

_____ grammar checkers

_____ math facts charts

_____ calculator

_____ With teacher cueing, the student will use sub vocalization (quietly repeating) to monitor and correct assignments.

_____ With teacher assistance and cueing, the student will review assignments and tests and analyze why responses or solutions were correct or incorrect.

_____ With teacher assistance, the student will listen to helpful suggestions that indicate what to do the next time.

_____ When the student is confronted with a problem that cannot be readily solved, the student will appropriately ask for help.

SECTION V

MEMORY PROBLEMS

MEMORY PROBLEMS

Tigers, Too (pp. 35-39, 131-148)

DIFFICULTY WITH WORKING MEMORY

Objective

To improve the student's ability to hold information temporarily in memory while tasks are performed and problems solved

Interventions

_____ With teacher scheduling, the student will complete tasks requiring working memory when optimally aroused.

_____ With teacher assistance and practice, the student will repeatedly use academic skills until they become permanent and automatic and increase working memory's processing space.

_____ With teacher instruction and practice, the student will use strategies that place fewer demands on working memory. The student will:
   _____ use a strategy which is congruent with the student's preferred learning style.
   _____ preview academic materials to be discussed during the following class lesson.
   _____ take notes in an alternate form (e.g., teacher-prepared outline, graphic organizer).
   _____ utilize a reading comprehension strategy.
   _____ employ a strategy to preplan, organize, execute, and edit written compositions and reports.
   _____ use a _____ math facts chart or _____ calculator.
   _____ use a cognitive cue card for the steps of math operations.
   _____ use a graphic organizer to solve math word problems.
   _____ use a problem-solving strategy to handle a new/unfamiliar/stressful social situation.

_____ With teacher instruction and practice, the student will appropriately ask for written directions and copies of assignment papers.

_____ With teacher instruction and practice, the student will learn and use strategies to help maintain information in working memory. The student will:
   _____ complete academic tasks in small segments.
   _____ associate new information with existing knowledge.
   _____ group information into meaningful categories.
   _____ rehearse/repeat/subvocalize information frequently.
   _____ answer open-ended questions.
   _____ paraphrase/summarize information at intervals.
   _____ use visualization strategies (e.g., drawing, diagrams, illustrations, graphic organizers).
   _____ learn through a combination of sensory modalities.
   _____ participate in small group discussions.

_____ The student will initiate asking the teacher for a strategy when needed.

DIFFICULTY ENCODING/CONSOLIDATING (LEARNING)

Objective

To improve the student's ability to master educational materials

Interventions

_____ With teacher instruction and practice, the student will utilize strategies congruent with individual learning preferences to encode information rather than using rote memorization. The student will use:

> _____ cognitive strategies specific to the material being learned.
> _____ verbal strategies.
>> _____ self-talk with inflection
>> _____ responding to open-ended questioning
>> _____ stories incorporating material
>> _____ acronyms
>> _____ acrostics
>> _____ abbreviations
>> _____ rhymes
>> _____ music
> _____ visual strategies.
>> _____ drawing
>> _____ graphic organizers
>> _____ editing strip
> _____ categorization.
> _____ combination of strategies _____

_____ With teacher assistance, the student will review learning materials:

> _____ 5-10 minutes after the lesson.
> _____ 24 hours later.
> _____ one month later.
> _____ at intervals during the school year.

_____ With teacher instruction and cueing, the student will do something different each time the material is studied.

_____ With teacher assistance and cueing, the student will place memory strategies in the strategy ("trick") book.

DIFFICULTY RETRIEVING (RECALLING)

Objective

To enhance the student's ability to retrieve information from long-term memory

Interventions

_____ With teacher assistance, the student will recall information on:
- _____ multiple-choice tests.
- _____ matching tests.
- _____ true-false tests.
- _____ open book tests.
- _____ take home tests.

_____ With teacher preparation, the student will demonstrate understanding of learning materials in an alternate form.
- _____ outline form on essay tests
- _____ oral presentation
- _____ visual presentation
- _____ with retrieval cues provided

_____ With teacher assistance, the student will respond to questioning with:
- _____ additional time provided.
- _____ questions furnished in advance.

_____ With teacher assistance, the student will use a word bank to answer fill-in-the-blank tests.

_____ With teacher assistance and cueing, the student will review learned strategies immediately prior to testing.

_____ With teacher cueing, the student will write the strategies on the back of the test as soon as it is received.

_____ With teacher cueing, the student will remember to turn in completed assignments.

DIFFICULTY WITH PROCEDURAL MEMORY

Objective

To improve the student's ability to automatically recall the steps/ sequences for performing academic tasks, completing assignments, and solving problems

Accommodations/Interventions

_____ With teacher assistance and practice, the student will use organizational strategies indicating the order in which academic skills should be executed. The appropriate strategies include following the steps for:

> _____ completing assignments.
> _____ finding main ideas and facts in narrative texts.
> _____ reading expository texts.
> _____ identifying main ideas and facts in expository texts.
> _____ writing narrative texts.
> _____ writing different expository texts.
> _____ completing long-term projects.
> _____ revising/editing written texts.
> _____ solving math operations/procedures.
> _____ answering the questions in math word problems.
> _____ studying for tests.

_____ With teacher assistance, cueing, and practice, the student will follow the steps required to complete assignments. The student will:

> _____ utilize a specified method for taking notes.
> _____ organize daily and weekly schedules and monthly calendars.
> _____ use a procedure for recording homework assignments.
> _____ follow steps for remembering to take home needed materials.
> _____ allocate and manage time for homework completion.
> _____ use a strategy for remembering to return homework to school and turn it in.
> _____ allocate and manage the time prior to testing.
> _____ determine the amount of time to be spent on individual test questions.

_____ With teacher assistance, practice, and cueing, the student will recall the sequence for solving problem situations. The student will follow the steps for:

> _____ using relaxation techniques to reduce anxiety/overarousal using a cognitive problem solving strategy.
> _____ following the who, what, when, where, why, and how sequence to understand negative social interactions.
> _____ focusing and sustaining attention during conversations.
> _____ controlling impulsive comments/actions.
> _____ organizing/sequencing conversations.
> _____ communicating with peers (greeting skills, joining group discussions, introducing friends, initiating and maintaining conversations, initiating social plans).

_____ understanding the feelings of self/others.

_____ negotiating and compromising.

DIFFICULTY WITH PROSPECTIVE MEMORY

Objective

To improve the student's ability to remember responsibilities and deadlines independently (remembering to remember)

Interventions

_____ With teacher assistance, the student will use daily and weekly schedules/planners and monthly calendars.

_____ The student will _____ select or _____ design the assignment book, weekly schedules, and monthly calendars.

_____ The student will use an electronic organizer. The student will choose:

      _____ a voice-activated model.

      _____ an organizer that provides external, time-based prompts (electronically activated screen, beeps, vibrations) to cue important activities.

      _____ a pocket-size electronic model that visually displays daily, and weekly schedules, and calendar on a screen.

_____ With teacher cueing, the student will use the daily, and weekly schedules, and monthly calendar or the electronic organizer.

_____ With teacher assistance and practice, the student will prepare short "To Do Lists" of the essential tasks that need to be carried out during the day, week, and month.

      _____ With teacher assistance and cueing, the student will discuss the list as it is being prepared.

_____ With teacher assistance, the student will transfer the "To Do List" to the daily and weekly schedules, and monthly calendar. The student will:

      _____ sequence activities in the order in which they occur throughout the day.

      _____ estimate and allocate the time it will take to complete the tasks and schedule accordingly.

      _____ schedule breaks between tasks.

      _____ note due dates and steps for completing long-term assignments and studying for tests.

      _____ highlight steps for completing a book report in one color, test dates in another color, etc.

_____ With teacher assistance, the student will place the daily, and weekly schedules, and monthly calendars in the front of the student's notebook.

Tigers, Too: Checklists © 2010 by Marilyn P. Dornbush, Ph.D., and Sheryl K. Pruitt, M.Ed., ET/P

_____ With teacher assistance, practice, and cueing, the student will follow the study schedule. The student will:

      _____ follow long-term schedules for completing reports, projects, and studying for tests.

      _____ determine whether the schedule is being followed correctly at frequently scheduled check points.

      _____ cross off tasks as they are completed.

DIFFICULTY WITH STRATEGIC MEMORY

Objective

To improve the student's ability to use strategies to increase understanding, complete assignments, solve problems, encode information, and facilitate retrieval

Interventions

_____ With teacher instruction and practice, the student will learn and use strategies congruent with the student's learning style to encode information rather than using rote memorization. The student will use:

      _____ cognitive strategies specific to the material being learned.

      _____ auditory strategies.

            _____ self-talk with inflection

            _____ responding to open-ended questioning

            _____ stories incorporating material

            _____ acronyms

            _____ acrostics

            _____ abbreviations

            _____ rhymes

            _____ music

      _____ visual strategies.

            _____ drawing

            _____ graphic organizers

            _____ editing strips

      _____ categorization.

      _____ combination of strategies _____

_____ With teacher assistance and cueing, the student will do something different each time the material is studied.

_____ With teacher assistance and cueing, the student will place the memory strategies and work samples in the strategy ("trick") book.

_____ With teacher assistance, the student will review the strategies throughout the school year.

_____ With teacher assistance and cueing, the student will review strategies immediately prior to testing.

_____ With teacher cueing, the student will write the strategies on the back of the test as soon as it is received.

DIFFICULTY WITH METAMEMORY

Objective

To increase the student's awareness of memory strengths and weaknesses and the need to use strategies to aid memory

Interventions

_____ With teacher assistance and practice, the student will identify individual memory strengths.

_____ With teacher assistance and practice, the student will analyze challenges or weaknesses that interfere with memory.

_____ With teacher assistance, the student will select an appropriate memory strategy, and predict performance prior to the recall task.
  _____ verbal rehearsal
  _____ mnemonic
  _____ visualization
  _____ link material to what is known
  _____ paraphrase material
  _____ rehearse through discussion and application

_____ With teacher assistance and cueing, the student will evaluate the effectiveness of the chosen strategy.

_____ With teacher assistance and cueing, the student will record the number of correct answers and compare the results over time.

SECTION VI

IMPAIRED ACADEMIC SKILLS

IMPAIRED ACADEMIC SKILLS

TIGERS, TOO (PP. 151-256, 379-401)

DIFFICULTY WITH ORAL EXPRESSION

Objective

To improve the ability to use pragmatic (social) language to communicate

Interventions

Accommodations and interventions for pragmatic language skills are listed in Social Skills (pp. 65-67).

DIFFICULTY WITH LISTENING COMPREHENSION

Objective

To improve the ability to understand lessons presented orally

Interventions

_____ With teacher, parental, and/or tutor assistance, the student will preview the concepts and facts to be discussed during the following lesson. The student will:

    _____ read material about the topic to be covered.

    _____ review notes from the previous lesson during homework.

    _____ read a list of questions to be answered during class.

    _____ examine a list of new vocabulary words that will be used and their definitions.

    _____ complete a pre-listening activity suggested by the teacher (e.g., perform an experiment, watch a video).

_____ When presented an oral lesson at the _____ grade <u>instructional</u> level, the student will with teacher cueing be able to:

    _____ express the main idea.

    _____ relate the sequence of the story.

    _____ answer factual questions.

    _____ answer inferential questions.

    _____ recognize similarities and differences.

    _____ predict outcomes.

    _____ interpret figurative language (e.g., idioms, clichés).

    _____ recognize multiple meanings.

    _____ recognize facts and opinions.

    _____ other _____

_____ When given _____ step directions with _____ verbal, _____ visual, or _____ cognitive cues, the student will be able to follow directions.

_____ When given oral instructions, the student will ask for:
    _____ repetition.
    _____ clarification.
    _____ directions to be written on the board.
    _____ an agreed-upon "buddy" to repeat the directions.

_____ When given oral directions, the student will subvocalize the instructions.

_____ With teacher assistance and practice, the student will use a structured system to take notes.

_____ With teacher assistance, the student who has handwriting problems will use a strategy to circumvent the problems associated with notetaking.
    _____ ask for a copy of the teacher's notes
    _____ select a peer who is a good note taker to share notes
    _____ ask a classmate to photocopy the notes
    _____ ask a peer to use carbonless duplicating paper
    _____ use a laptop computer

_____ With teacher assistance and practice, the student with working memory problems will take notes by completing:
    _____ the teacher's lesson plan.
    _____ a teacher-prepared mind map.
    _____ a teacher-prepared graphic organizer.
    _____ a teacher-prepared outline.

_____ With teacher assistance and practice, the student will learn and use abbreviations to improve notetaking skills.

_____ With teacher assistance, cueing, and practice, the student after an oral lesson will:
    _____ summarize or restate the most important information.
    _____ review and correct notes.
    _____ organize the material into a graphic organizer.
    _____ answer and discuss teacher-prepared questions.
    _____ generate questions to ask other students.

DIFFICULTY ACQUIRING BASIC READING SKILLS

Objective

To improve the student's basic reading skills to the _____ reading level

Interventions

_____ With teacher assistance, the student will use reading materials consistent with individual learning style preferences.

     _____ auditory

     _____ visual-spatial

     _____ kinesthetic (tactile)

     _____ logical

     _____ interpersonal

     _____ intrapersonal

     _____ musical

_____ The student will use a research-based reading program to learn phonemic awareness, phonics, and fluency.

     Title of program: _____

_____ The student will complete classroom reading lessons at the student's <u>instructional</u> level (_____ grade level).

_____ The student will complete seat work and homework at the student's <u>independent</u> level (_____ grade level).

_____ With teacher providing cognitive cues and practice, the student will master decoding skills at an automatic level.

_____ When given passages to read, the student will improve fluency by:

     _____ looking over the material before reading it aloud.

     _____ previewing sight words and vocabulary.

     _____ using a pointer to assist with more efficient tracking.

     _____ reading in a small group.

     _____ using a repeated reading technique.

     _____ reading with partners (teacher, parent, older student) and:

          _____ listening as the partners read.

          _____ taking turns reading orally and listening.

          _____ reading in unison.

_____ When assigned passages to read, the student will use:

     _____ a finger, marker, or index card darkened in the upper left corner to follow passages without skipping words or lines.

     _____ color overlays of the student's choice.

This page may be reprinted for classroom and personal, non-commercial use only.

Tigers, Too: Checklists © 2010 by Marilyn P. Dornbush, Ph.D., and Sheryl K. Pruitt, M.Ed., ET/P

43

_____ The student will use an "errorless learning" method to learn word recognition skills.

_____ With teacher assistance and practice, the student will master the basic sight words. The student will use:
  _____ "backward chaining."
  _____ repetition, drill, and practice.
  _____ flash cards.
  _____ word games.

_____ With teacher assistance, the student will increase automaticity of word recognition skills and the basic sight vocabulary. The student will:
  _____ master one skill (90%) before trying to learn another skill.
  _____ repeatedly use the skill.
  _____ continually review the skill.

_____ The student will use computer reading programs to reinforce the learning of word recognition skills and basic sight vocabulary.

_____ The student will receive individualized instruction from a teacher who is trained to remediate problems associated with the acquisition of basic reading skills.

DIFFICULTY WITH READING COMPREHENSION

Objective

To improve the student's reading comprehension to the _____ grade level

Interventions

_____ With teacher assistance, the student will read during classroom lessons comprehension materials at the student's <u>instructional</u> level (_____ grade level).

_____ With teacher assistance, the student will complete reading comprehension seatwork and homework at the student's <u>independent</u> level (_____ grade level).

_____ With teacher assistance, the student will read comprehension materials congruent with the student's learning style preferences and interests.
  _____ auditory
  _____ visual-spatial
  _____ kinesthetic (tactile)
  _____ logical
  _____ interpersonal
  _____ intrapersonal

_____ The student will use one period each day to read for enjoyment. The student will:

    _____ read in a comfortable reading area.

    _____ read short, interesting books.

    _____ use computer reading programs.

    _____ use an e-book reader.

    _____ listen to books on tape/CD/MP3.

    _____ use earphones to block out distractions.

_____ With teacher, parental, and/or tutor assistance, the student will preview the concepts and facts to be read during the following lesson. The student will:

    _____ examine a list of new vocabulary words that will be used and their definitions.

    _____ read material about the topic to be covered (e.g., newspapers, magazines, trade manuals).

    _____ complete a pre-listening activity suggested by the teacher (e.g., do an experiment, watch a video or movie).

    _____ use a study guide to preview information.

_____ With teacher instruction and practice, the student will learn different text structures (narrative, expository).

_____ When assigned passages to read at the appropriate instructional level, the student will:

    _____ highlight primary details (who, what, when, where, how, why) in text.

    _____ underline key words.

    _____ paraphrase and summarize reading materials.

    _____ use verbal and/or visual strategies to aid recall.

    _____ use graphic organizers (e.g., mind map, Venn diagram, timeline) to organize information.

    _____ use pictorial cues to organize information in passages.

    _____ use charts, graphs, and/or diagrams to depict information.

_____ After reading comprehension passages that have been read orally or silently, the student will be asked to:

    _____ define new vocabulary words.

    _____ summarize main ideas.

    _____ identify essential facts.

    _____ review organization/sequence of material.

    _____ make inferences.

    _____ make predictions.

    _____ interpret cause-and-effect situations.

    _____ discuss similarities and differences between people, places, events, concepts, etc.

    _____ answer teacher-prepared questions.

    _____ generate questions to ask classmates.

_____ With teacher assistance and practice, the student will self-monitor comprehension of reading materials. The student will:

      _____ read aloud.

      _____ tape record passages and listen while reading the text.

      _____ paraphrase or summarize the material.

      _____ use self-questioning.

_____ When classmates are asked to read aloud, the student will <u>not</u> be required to read orally if the task exacerbates the symptoms associated with the disorder(s).

_____ With teacher assistance and practice, the student will increase the capacity of working memory for the comprehension of reading materials. The student will use:

      _____ association of new concepts with existing knowledge.

      _____ verbal rehearsal of main ideas and facts.

      _____ paraphrasing and summarizing.

      _____ categorization (putting new information into existing categories).

      _____ visualization.

_____ When symptoms of ADHD, TS, and/or OCD interfere with reading, the student will:

      _____ ask for the material to be read aloud by teacher, aide, or another student.

      _____ listen to recorded books.

      _____ use a computer reading program.

      _____ use an e-book reader.

_____ The student will use computer reading programs to reinforce reading comprehension skills.

_____ The student will receive individualized instruction from a teacher who is trained to remediate reading comprehension problems.

DIFFICULTY WITH WRITTEN EXPRESSION

Objective

To improve the student's written expression skills in: _____ sentences, _____ paragraphs, _____ narrative writing, _____ expository writing, _____ functional writing to a _____ grade level

Interventions

_____ With teacher assistance, the student who has handwriting problems will use alternative methods. The student will:

    _____ use _____ manuscript or _____ cursive writing.

    _____ utilize computer technology (e.g., word processing, voice-activated software) to produce written assignments.

    _____ dictate compositions to a "scribe."

    _____ dictate into a tape recorder.

    _____ answer _____ multiple-choice, _____ matching, _____ true-false questions rather than short answer or essay questions.

    _____ create a model, a poster, and/or a scrapbook.

    _____ present information orally.

_____ With teacher assistance and practice, the student who has difficulty spelling when writing will receive individualized spelling instruction. The student will:

    _____ learn the basic sight words using a multi-sensory approach (look, say, write, check, write again).

    _____ master phonetically-based words and word parts.

    _____ use a pretest-study-post test rather than a study-test procedure.

    _____ utilize the computer spell checker.

    _____ use an electronic spell check to correct misspellings.

_____ With teacher assistance and practice, the student will learn and use prewriting strategies (brainstorming, prioritizing, organizing, sequencing, managing time). The student will:

    _____ propose (brainstorm, generate) ideas for a topic.

        _____ activate knowledge and personal experience

        _____ use a mind mapping strategy to stimulate ideas

    _____ generate ideas on the computer.

    _____ use teacher-prepared prompts.

    _____ tape record ideas.

    _____ define the purpose for writing.

    _____ rank order the ideas.

    _____ identify the most appropriate text structure for the topic (narrative, expository).

    _____ divide the writing assignment into stages and make a timetable for completing each part.

_____ With teacher assistance and practice, the student will follow the steps for writing a paper. The student will:

      _____ write the first draft on the computer.

      _____ write the title at the top of the page.

      _____ write an introductory paragraph that states and defines the topic.

      _____ write the following paragraphs presenting main ideas and facts.

      _____ write the concluding paragraph.

_____ With teacher assistance and practice, the student will write:

      _____ 1 paragraph.

      _____ 3 paragraphs.

      _____ 5 paragraphs.

      _____ essay/composition.

      _____ term paper.

_____ With teacher assistance and practice, the student will revise the content of writing assignments with a revision checklist.

_____ With teacher assistance and practice, the student will edit the mechanics of the writing using a:

      _____ visual editing strip.

      _____ cognitive strategy (e.g., COPS).

      _____ spell checker.

      _____ grammar checker.

      _____ dictionary.

      _____ thesaurus.

      _____ personal editor (parent, teacher, older student).

_____ The student will appropriately ask for help when experiencing difficulty with written expression.

_____ The student will receive individualized instruction from a teacher who is trained to remediate written expression problems.

DIFFICULTY WITH MATH COMPUTATIONS

Objective

To improve the student's math calculation skills to the _____ grade level

Interventions

_____ With teacher assistance, the student who has handwriting problems will use alternative methods. The student will:

    _____ complete untimed math assignments.

    _____ solve a reduced number of problems (e.g., every other problem).

    _____ work problems on teacher-prepared or duplicated copies of the math assignment.

    _____ use a grid, column paper, or graph paper to facilitate alignment.

_____ The student will complete math classroom lessons at the instructional level (_____ grade level).

_____ The student will complete math seat work and homework at the independent level (_____ grade level).

_____ With teacher instruction, the student will use an "errorless learning" method to master the basic math facts.

_____ With teacher instruction and practice, the student will learn the math facts at an automatic level (90% mastery).

_____ With teacher instruction, practice, and cueing, the student will use cognitive cues to learn the math facts.

    _____ addition

    _____ subtraction

    _____ multiplication

    _____ division

_____ With teacher cueing, the student will use a calculator or math facts chart to solve basic arithmetic problems.

_____ With teacher instruction and assistance, the student will use concrete objects and real-life situations to learn abstract math concepts and procedures.

_____ The student will demonstrate mastery of a computational skill nine out of ten times over an extended period before being introduced to a new skill.

_____ The student will use a highlighter to identify operational signs.

_____ With teacher cueing, the student will read calculation problems aloud before completing the operations.

_____ With teacher cueing, the student will calculate multi-step problems using a cognitive strategy to assist recall of the steps and sequence of the operations.

_____ With teacher cueing, the student will subvocalize problems while solving the problems.

_____ With teacher intervention and checking, the student will demonstrate understanding of assignments by working the first two or three problems.

_____ The student will appropriately ask for help when math concepts and procedures are not understood.

_____ With teacher assistance and practice, the student will check the accuracy of the calculations by:

      _____ comparing it to an estimate.

      _____ using a cognitive strategy with a visual editing cue card.

      _____ using a math editing checklist for computations.

      _____ using a calculator.

_____ With teacher cueing, the student will consult examples in the strategy ("trick") book when computational procedures cannot be recalled.

_____ The student will use computer math programs to practice routine, repetitive math problems (math facts, computations) otherwise completed with pencil and paper.

_____ The student will receive individualized instruction from a teacher who is trained to remediate problems associated with the acquisition of basic math skills.

DIFFICULTY WITH MATH REASONING

Objective

To improve the student's math reasoning skills to the _____ grade level

Interventions

_____ The student will complete classroom lessons at the <u>instructional</u> level (_____ grade level).

_____ The student will complete seat work and homework at the <u>independent</u> level (_____ grade level).

_____ With teacher instruction and assistance, the student will use concrete objects and real-life situations to solve abstract word problems.

_____ With teacher assistance, the student will complete _____ one-step, _____ two-step, _____ three-step problems.

_____ With teacher instruction, assistance, and cueing, the student will use an organized, step-by-step strategy for solving word problems. The student will:

_____ read the word problem aloud before solving it.

_____ subvocalize steps of the word problem while solving it.

_____ underline or highlight cue words which identify the operation to be used.

_____ cross out information that is not relevant.

_____ paraphrase the questions to be answered.

_____ diagram or draw pictures to illustrate word problems.

_____ analyze and select the best strategy to use.

_____ estimate answers.

_____ The student will appropriately ask for help when the word problems are not understood.

_____ With teacher cueing, the student will independently solve word problems.

_____ With teacher instruction and practice, the student will be able to correctly solve problems involving:

_____ fractions.

_____ decimals.

_____ percentages.

_____ money.

_____ measurement.

_____ time.

_____ With teacher assistance, practice, and cueing, the student will check the accuracy of the answers by:

_____ using a math editing checklist for word problems.

_____ using a calculator.

_____ With teacher cueing, the student will consult examples in the strategy ("trick") book when word problem solving strategies are forgotten.

_____ The student will use computer math programs to practice solving word problems.

_____ The student will receive individualized instruction from a teacher who is trained to remediate problems associated with math reasoning skills.

SECTION VII

INEFFICIENT STUDY SKILLS

INEFFICIENT STUDY SKILLS

Tigers, Too (pp. 259-290)

NOTETAKING

Objective

To minimize the student's difficulty taking notes in class

Interventions

_____ With teacher assistance, the student will implement a strategy to circumvent handwriting problems associated with notetaking.

      _____ choose a peer or "buddy" to share the notes

      _____ ask a classmate to photocopy the notes

      _____ ask a peer to use lined carbonless duplicating paper and give the copy to the student

      _____ complete teacher-prepared outlines

      _____ finish teacher-prepared graphic organizers

      _____ fill in teacher-prepared notes or lesson plans

      _____ use a laptop computer

_____ With teacher instruction, the student will practice and use a structured notetaking system.

_____ With instruction, assistance, and cueing, the student will review the notes immediately after the lesson.

      _____ fill in missed information

      _____ make sure the notes are understandable

      _____ ask for further clarification

      _____ borrow and compare the notes from another student

_____ With teacher instruction, assistance, and cueing, the student will use a strategy to learn the information in the notes.

      _____ star, _____ highlight, or _____ underline important concepts and facts with different color pencils

      _____ create visual organizers

      _____ reorganize or outline the notes

      _____ summarize and reword the most salient information

      _____ rehearse aloud the content of the lesson

      _____ formulate questions to be asked on a test

      _____ make notecards (flash cards)

_____ With teacher assistance and cueing, the student will ask a classmate for notes missed during an absence.

HOMEWORK

Objective

To enhance the student's ability to complete assigned, meaningful homework

Interventions

_____ The student will complete homework that has been assigned at the student's <u>independent</u> level (_____ grade level).

_____ The student will complete homework as a means of practicing previously taught materials.

_____ With teacher assistance, the student will complete alternate forms of homework to _____ bypass handwriting problems and/or _____ minimize attentional difficulties. The student will:

    _____ play educational games relating to the assignment.

    _____ complete hands-on projects.

    _____ work with another student who has a similar interest in the topic.

    _____ read assigned magazine articles with color photographs.

    _____ watch a video about the subject and write questions to ask the other students the following day.

    _____ access related information on the computer and report to the class during the next lesson.

_____ With teacher assistance and cueing, the student will use an assignment notebook. The student will:

    _____ record homework assignments at a scheduled time each day.

    _____ have the teacher or a peer determine if the homework instructions were recorded correctly.

    _____ prepare a "To Do List" to prioritize, organize, and consolidate the homework assignments, long-term projects, and test preparations that need to be completed each day, week, and month.

    _____ write down the time needed to complete each assignment and check the accuracy of the estimates when the tasks are finished.

    _____ schedule hardest, least liked tasks at the beginning of the homework session.

    _____ enter the "To Do List" into the assignment book.

    _____ color coordinate assignment sheets with textbooks and folders.

    _____ cross off assignments as they are completed.

_____ With teacher assistance and cueing, the student will take the needed materials home. The student will:

    _____ leave class a few minutes before dismissal to go to the locker and pack the school bag.

    _____ have the needed materials checked by an aide or resource teacher.

_____ With teacher instruction, the student will access homework assignments on the classroom/ school homework website.

_____ With teacher assistance, the student will complete homework that has been scanned into the student's computer.

_____ With teacher assistance and cueing, the student will turn in completed homework. The student will:

      _____ place the homework in a predetermined location in the classroom.

      _____ respond to a reminder at the beginning of class to turn in an assignment.

_____ The student will return homework via the Internet.

_____ With teacher permission, the student will turn in homework late and receive credit when the parents indicate that the symptoms of the disorder(s) interfered with homework completion.

_____ The student will attend _____ an after-school study group or _____ a study period when completing homework at home is presenting problems.

TEST PREPARATION

Objective

To improve the student's ability to study for tests

Interventions

_____ With teacher instruction, the student will learn individually appropriate study skills.

      _____ The student with verbal strengths will master educational materials by:

            _____ explaining difficult concepts to others.

            _____ incorporating information into a story.

            _____ making acronyms.

            _____ creating acrostics.

            _____ setting new information to music.

            _____ forming a study group.

      _____ The student with nonverbal strengths will master educational materials by:

            _____ completing graphic organizers.

            _____ creating images relating to the information.

            _____ drawing pictures.

            _____ using a mind map.

            _____ making flash cards.

_____ With teacher assistance, practice, and cueing, the student will use advance notice of tests to organize and prepare for tests. The student will:

      _____ allocate and manage time prior to testing.

      _____ write test dates in the assignment book and weekly and monthly calendars.

      _____ decide how much time will be needed to learn the material.

      _____ review information/class notes as part of daily and weekly sessions.

_____ With teacher instruction and practice, the student will use self-testing.

SECTION VIII

DIFFICULTY TAKING TESTS

DIFFICULTY TAKING TESTS

Tigers, Too (pp. 293-303)

Objective

To improve the student's ability to successfully take tests

Interventions

_____ With teacher assistance, the student will take tests in an alternate setting/environment.
   _____ individually
   _____ near the test administrator
   _____ in the back of the classroom
   _____ in a small group
   _____ in a study carrel
   _____ with noise buffers to minimize extraneous distractions
   _____ in the special education classroom
   _____ in another school setting

Specify: _____

_____ With teacher intervention, the student will follow modified timing/scheduling of tests.
   _____ at the time most beneficial to the student
      _____ start of school day
      _____ late morning
      _____ early afternoon
   _____ with periodic movement breaks of up to _____ minutes (e.g., 10 or 20 minutes)
   _____ in several sessions
   _____ with extended time limits
   _____ with no time limits

_____ With teacher assistance, the student will take tests administered by the:
   _____ classroom teacher.
   _____ special education teacher.
   _____ another member of school staff.

Specify: _____

_____ With teacher assistance, the student will take standardized tests with modifications.

_____ With teacher intervention and assistance, the student will follow directions which will be:
   _____ provided in a written format.
   _____ highlighted/underlined by _____ teacher, _____ student.
   _____ read orally.
   _____ repeated as necessary.
   _____ restated by the student.

Tigers, Too: Checklists © 2010 by Marilyn P. Dornbush, Ph.D., and Sheryl K. Pruitt, M.Ed., ET/P

_____ With teacher intervention, the student will take tests administered with:

     _____ increased space between test items.

     _____ reduced number of test items per page.

     _____ increased size of answer bubbles or answer blocks.

     _____ multiple-choice questions listed in vertical order with answer bubbles to the right of items.

_____ With teacher intervention, the student will take tests administered in a:

     _____ multiple-choice format.

     _____ fill-in-the-blank format.

     _____ true/false format.

     _____ short answer format.

     _____ essay format.

     _____ open-book format.

     _____ take-home test format.

_____ With teacher assistance, the student will utilize:

     _____ word banks for fill-in-the-blank tests.

     _____ cognitive cue cards.

     _____ graphic organizers.

     _____ place markers to assist tracking.

     _____ a math facts chart.

     _____ a calculator.

_____ With teacher assistance, the student will:

     _____ mark/circle answers in test booklets to be transferred to the computer-scored sheet by an adult.

     _____ mark answers on tests scanned into the student's computer.

     _____ take tests orally.

     _____ have answers recorded/recopied/verified by a scribe.

     _____ review recorded answers and revise as needed.

     _____ use a computer with a word processing program.

     _____ use a spell check or grammar check device.

     _____ tape record answers.

     _____ answer essay questions in outline form.

     _____ demonstrate mastery with _____ completion of a project, _____ computer presentation, _____ oral report.

SECTION IX

IMPAIRED SOCIAL SKILLS

IMPAIRED SOCIAL SKILLS

TIGERS, TOO (PP. 307-338)

Objective

To improve the student's ability to use age-appropriate social skills

Interventions

_____ With teacher assistance, the student will participate in cooperative learning experiences to optimize social interactions. Using special interests and talents, the student will act as group:

      _____ secretary.

      _____ artist.

      _____ computer expert.

      _____ research specialist.

      _____ oral presenter.

      _____ leader.

      _____ other _____

_____ When discussing a topic or having a conversation, the student will be able to:

      _____ greet peers and adults.

          _____ face the speaker and employ a strategy for appearing to make eye contact

          _____ become a member of an ongoing group conversation

          _____ introduce a friend

          _____ use a prearranged greeting script

      _____ initiate conversations.

      _____ communicate intent (state purpose).

      _____ organize and sequence communications.

      _____ stay on topic (in increasing increments).

      _____ return to the topic of conversation.

          _____ with teacher cueing

          _____ without teacher cueing

      _____ cue the listener to a topic change.

      _____ listen when the other person is speaking.

      _____ decrease interruptions.

      _____ follow turn-taking rules.

      _____ show interest by:

          _____ nodding head.

          _____ making a relevant comment.

          _____ paraphrasing what was said.

          _____ asking questions.

      _____ respond tactfully.

      _____ use clarifying strategies when misunderstood.

      _____ use conversation closers to end a conversation.

This page may be reprinted for classroom and personal, non-commercial use only.

Tigers, Too: Checklists © 2010 by Marilyn P. Dornbush, Ph.D., and Sheryl K. Pruitt, M.Ed., ET/P

65

_____ With teacher instruction and assistance, the student will:
_____ verbalize and use a strategy for maintaining the correct social distance between people (arm's length).
_____ touch others appropriately.

_____ With teacher instruction and assistance, the student will communicate feelings (mad, sad, glad, scared) to others by using the appropriate:
_____ tone of voice.
_____ volume of voice.
_____ intensity of voice.
_____ facial features.
_____ gestures.
_____ body language.

_____ With teacher instruction and assistance, the student will identify the verbal feelings being expressed by others. The student will listen to the:
_____ tone of voice.
_____ volume of voice.
_____ intensity of voice.

_____ With teacher instruction and assistance, the student will identify the nonverbal feelings being expressed by others. The student will observe the:
_____ facial features.
_____ gestures.
_____ body language.

_____ With teacher instruction, assistance, and cueing, the student will recognize when it is time to change the topic of conversation. The student will:
_____ determine whether the classmates are listening.
_____ make one comment per turn.
_____ learn and use transition words.
_____ signal a change in topic.
_____ respond to cues indicating the need for a change in topic.

_____ With teacher assistance, the student will practice using age-appropriate language with _____ classmates, _____same sex peers, _____ teachers, and _____ other adults.

_____ With teacher assistance and practice, the student will use appropriate language to communicate respect for others. The student will:
_____ ask others how they feel.
_____ make positive statements related to the emotions being expressed.
_____ compliment others.
_____ learn a script for giving compliments.
_____ share information without bragging or boasting.

_____ With teacher assistance, the student will communicate needs to others.

_____ With teacher instruction and practice, the student will learn and use perspective-taking skills. The student will:

      _____ listen to what is being said.

      _____ paraphrase what was said.

      _____ observe and interpret nonverbal cues.

      _____ discuss whether the other student might perceive the situation differently.

      _____ propose alternative interpretations.

_____ With teacher assistance, the student will recognize and identify the expectations of others.

_____ With teacher assistance, the student will recognize and identify social interaction problems. The student will:

      _____ use who, what, when, where, how, and why questions to understand the nature of the problems.

      _____ discuss consequences of previous behaviors (positive and negative) in similar situations.

_____ With teacher assistance, the student will use executive skills to solve social problems. The student will:

      _____ correctly identify social problems to be addressed.

      _____ set realistic goals.

      _____ brainstorm solutions to the problems.

      _____ analyze the consequences of each proposed idea.

      _____ decide on and use the best strategy.

      _____ self-monitor the implementation of the strategy and make corrections as needed.

_____ With teacher instruction and assistance, the student will utilize a strategy for accepting and internalizing positive statements about one's self.

_____ With teacher instruction and assistance, the student will make positive self-statements.

_____ With teacher instruction and assistance, the student will use verbal, visual, and cognitive strategies to self-monitor impulse control in social situations (e.g., interrupting, intruding in others' games).

_____ When confronted with an emotionally charged social situation, the student will leave the setting in a previously agreed-upon manner (_____) and go to a predetermined safe place (_____) to release frustration and anger.

_____ With teacher assistance and cueing, the student will, after a "storm" has ended and control has been restored, _____ apologize, or _____ mend a damaged peer, teacher, and/or adult relationship.

Tigers, Too: Checklists © 2010 by Marilyn P. Dornbush, Ph.D., and Sheryl K. Pruitt, M.Ed., ET/P

_____ With teacher instruction and assistance, the student will correctly identify the effect the inappropriate behavior had on self and others.

SECTION X

SCHOOL PERSONNEL INTERVENTIONS

REFERRALS

SCHOOL PERSONNEL INTERVENTIONS/REFERRALS

SCHOOL PERSONNEL INTERVENTIONS

_____ With student and parent permission, school personnel will make arrangements for staff awareness programs.

_____ With student and parent permission, school personnel will make arrangements for peer awareness programs.

_____ The teacher will attend a professional conference relating to the student's disorder(s).

_____ School personnel will establish and monitor a school-wide anti-bullying policy.

_____ The teacher will identify and present information, materials, tasks, and activities in the student's preferred learning style(s).

_____ Logical/Verbal	_____ Musical
_____ Visual-Spatial	_____ Interpersonal
_____ Tactile/Kinesthetic	_____ Intrapersonal
_____ Logical/Mathematical	

_____ The teacher will help the student select a compatible "buddy."
- _____ note-taking "buddy"
- _____ assignment/project completion "buddy"
- _____ homework "buddy"
- _____ hall "buddy"
- _____ cafeteria "buddy"
- _____ playground "buddy"
- _____ bus "buddy"

_____ The teacher will provide assistance and make handwriting accommodations by:
- _____ extending time limits.
- _____ eliminating time limits.
- _____ modifying expectations by:
  - _____ reducing the number of questions.
  - _____ accepting short answers.
  - _____ permitting an outline of the answers.
  - _____ providing a photocopy of the lecture notes.
- _____ permitting the use of _____ manuscript or _____ cursive writing.
- _____ pre-printing assignment papers (e.g., written directions, assignment sequences).
- _____ allowing work to be finished in segments and at different times.
- _____ providing partially filled-in graphic organizers to be completed.
- _____ arranging for assignments to be dictated to a "scribe."
- _____ permitting dictation into a tape recorder.

_____ allowing use of computer technology (e.g., word processing program, voice-activated software).

_____ giving _____ multiple-choice, _____ matching, or _____ true-false tests instead of short answer or essay questions.

_____ other _____

_____ The teacher will provide preferential seating according to the student's needs. The student will be provided seating:

_____ away from distractions.

_____ in close proximity to door so an unobtrusive exit can be made when needed.

_____ at the back of the room.

_____ near students who will not provide distractions or stimulate inappropriate behaviors.

_____ in two different locations so movement can be made.

_____ in a carrel while completing assignments to eliminate distractions.

_____ The teacher will assign a locker that uses _____ a lock with a key or _____ a combination lock that requires no reverse sequencing. The teacher will:

_____ provide an alternative location to store books and materials if the student has difficulty using a locker.

_____ To circumvent disorganization and forgetfulness, the student will be provided:

_____ extra workspace to spread out materials (larger desk/table).

_____ a list of necessary materials for assignments/activities.

_____ an extra supply of materials, such as pencils and paper (provided by the parents at beginning of school year).

_____ extra sets of books (one to be used in the classroom and the other at home).

_____ color-coded textbooks, notebooks, and folders so that each subject is color coordinated (e.g., red history book cover corresponds with the red history notebook and red folder).

_____ assignments written on color coordinated paper.

_____ The teacher will provide mobility options to _____ increase arousal and attention, to _____ decrease restlessness and overactivity, and/or to _____ reduce anxiety and overarousal. The student will be allowed to:

_____ change work sites.

_____ make a trip to the office.

_____ take a note to another teacher.

_____ pass out/collect classroom materials.

_____ doodle.

_____ use a small squeeze toy.

_____ take a short movement break (e.g., stand, reach for sky, touch toes, twist waist).

_____ exercise muscles and joints (e.g., press hands together, do chair pushups, push against the wall, carry reasonably heavy box to office).

_____ other _____

_____ The teacher will establish, post, explain, and reinforce positive classroom rules.

_____ The teacher will create a structured classroom schedule.

_____ The teacher will point out and discuss the schedule frequently throughout the day.

_____ The teacher will cue the student prior to giving directions to gain attention.

_____ The teacher will take into consideration the student's learning style when delivering instructions. The teacher will:
    _____ write directions on the board.
    _____ highlight critical words in the directions.
    _____ provide oral directions:
        _____ in single rather than multiple steps.
        _____ with pauses between each step.
        _____ at a slower than normal rate.
        _____ with repetition and rephrasing of the instructions.
    _____ incorporate a variety of modalities (e.g., verbal and written directions).

_____ The teacher will check understanding of instructions by:
    _____ discreetly asking the student to restate the directions.
    _____ asking the student to complete one step of the assignment.
    _____ asking the student to work one problem and have it checked before continuing.

_____ The teacher will provide the _____ parents, _____ resource teacher, _____ tutor with the class syllabus.

_____ The teacher will structure learning experiences that reduce the chance of failure. The teacher will:
    _____ present lessons at the student's <u>instructional</u> level (_____ grade level).
    _____ assign seatwork at the student's <u>independent</u> level (_____ grade level).
    _____ assign no work at the <u>frustration</u> level (_____ grade level).

_____ The teacher will schedule core academic subjects in the _____ late morning or _____ early afternoon.

_____ The teacher will introduce novelty or do something unusual to gain attention before beginning a lesson.

_____ The teacher will allow for fluctuations in attention by repeating, rephrasing, or summarizing information periodically.

_____ The teacher will prompt on-task behavior by:
    _____ touching the student's desk.
    _____ touching a sticker placed on the student's desk.
    _____ saying a code word.
    _____ touching the paper on which the student is working.

_____ The teacher will teach and use cognitive strategies to enhance mastery of academic materials.

_____ The teacher will positively reinforce the student's use of strategies.

_____ The teacher will divide long-term assignments into manageable stages and make a timetable for completion of each part.

_____ The teacher will monitor progress of long-term assignments.

_____ The teacher will grade assignments on the student's abilities rather than disabilities (e.g., subject content not handwriting or spelling).

_____ The teacher will adjust expectations when the severity of the symptoms associated with the disorder(s) increase. The teacher will:

    _____ assign short tasks and require accuracy and quality of response.

    _____ eliminate timed assignments.

    _____ postpone testing.

    _____ review previously learned material.

    _____ suggest use of the computer to reinforce skills.

_____ The teacher will provide warnings (15 minutes, 10 minutes, 5 minutes) prior to the end of a task (e.g., class assignment, test).

_____ The teacher will give advance notice before:

    _____ changing to a different schedule.

    _____ transitioning to a different task or activity.

_____ The teacher will utilize a communication log/assignment book or electronically contact parents regarding the student's academic and social progress on a _____ daily or a _____ weekly basis.

_____ The teacher will schedule a designated time each day to record homework assignments, organize materials, and locate belongings.

_____ The teacher will allow the student to go to the locker a few minutes before dismissal. The teacher will:

    _____ place a list of needed homework materials at eye level inside the locker.

    _____ cue the student to use the list to determine if the items are in the school bag.

    _____ check the school bag to make sure the necessary items for homework are included.

_____ The teacher will assign all homework at the student's <u>independent</u> level (_____ grade level).

_____ The teacher will assign homework that can be completed with a minimum of stress.
The teacher will:

    _____ take into consideration physical and emotional consequences of the neurological disorder(s) and their impact on the ability to quickly and efficiently complete homework.

    _____ modify the requirements/length of homework assignments if they frequently lead to frustration and agitation at home.

        _____ assign shorter homework assignments and require accuracy and quality of response

        _____ separate long-term assignments into small segments

        _____ vary the types of assignments

        _____ offer interesting alternatives to handwritten homework assignments

    _____ avoid assigning extra homework as a punishment technique.

    _____ arrange for unfinished class assignments to be completed at school rather than at home.

    _____ provide _____ after school study groups or _____ study periods to complete homework.

_____ The teacher will use a homework survey to determine the impact homework is having on the student and family.

_____ The teacher will establish a specific and consistent procedure for assigning homework.
The teacher will:

    _____ post assignments in the same location every day.

    _____ set a specific time during the day to record homework.

_____ The teacher will intervene when the student has difficulty recording homework accurately.
The teacher will:

    _____ give the student a copy of the homework assignments.

    _____ suggest a homework "buddy" to write down assignments.

    _____ scan homework papers that need to be completed into the student's computer.

    _____ create a homework Internet site that the student and the parents can access.

    _____ email parents regarding homework and deadlines/instructions for long-term assignments.

_____ The teacher will discuss homework expectations with the parents. The teacher will explain:

     _____ how frequently homework will be assigned.

     _____ the type of homework that will be given.

     _____ how long each homework assignment should take.

     _____ expected parental involvement.

          _____ provide assistance

          _____ carefully check the work and insist on corrections

          _____ make sure work is completed and returned to school

_____ The teacher will establish a specific procedure for collecting homework.

Specify: _____

_____ The teacher will permit homework to be returned via the Internet.

_____ The teacher will incorporate social skills training into the daily curriculum.
The teacher will:

     _____ design interventions consistent with the student's cognitive learning style:
(e.g., use of discussions, role playing, visual materials, written scripts).

     _____ provide assistance with peer interactions.

     _____ teach the use of anger management techniques.

     _____ teach and practice awareness of and bodily reaction to the student's own emotions.

     _____ teach and develop the student's sensitivity towards peers' feelings.

     _____ teach and practice interpreting classmates' _____ verbal and _____ nonverbal social
cues.

     _____ teach and practice strategies to minimize interrupting and difficulty waiting to take
a turn.

     _____ teach the student how to organize/sequence communications.

     _____ increase recognition of when it is time to change topic.

     _____ teach and practice perspective-taking skills.

     _____ teach and practice strategies for initiating and maintaining friendships.

     _____ teach and use a cognitive problem-solving strategy to resolve negative social
situations.

     _____ design _____ cooperative learning experiences and _____ educational games to
provide opportunities to interact and use communication skills.

     _____ create an exit strategy to a safe place when the student becomes over aroused.

     _____ discreetly offer academic and social suggestions that indicate what to do the next
time to be successful.

_____ The teacher will prepare tests to analyze which skills need to be practiced or retaught.
The teacher will:

      _____ balance questions between understanding and factual recall.

      _____ give sufficient notice of tests to provide ample time to organize and prepare for tests.

      _____ point out and _____ create study guides which indicate the most important information to be studied for tests.

      _____ identify types of questions to be asked.

      _____ indicate how the test will be graded and how much the test will count toward the final grade.

_____ The teacher will base the student's grades on several tests administered throughout the term rather than a single test at the end of the grading period.

_____ The teacher will adjust scoring criteria by allowing the student to:

      _____ re-answer incorrect responses for bonus points towards a higher grade.

      _____ retake the test until a passing grade is achieved.

      _____ receive partial credit.

      _____ be awarded points based on effort.

_____ The teacher will schedule make-up work and tests.

REFERRALS

_____ The teacher will refer the student to a school counselor for:

      _____ counseling.

      _____ a peer group for students with the same disabilities.

      _____ social skills development group.

_____ School personnel will refer the student for:

      _____ an assistive technology evaluation.

      _____ a speech and language evaluation.

      _____ an occupational therapy evaluation.

      _____ a psychoeducational evaluation.

      _____ a neuropsychological evaluation.